Maths C ...

Developing children's listening skills in the Daily Maths Lesson

YEAR
1

Peter Clarke

Published by Collins Educational
An imprint of HarperCollins*Publishers* Ltd
77-85 Fulham Palace Road
Hammersmith
London
W6 8JB

www.**Collins**Education.com
On-line Support for Schools and Colleges

First published 2002

10 9 8 7 6 5 4

ISBN 0 00 713 351 0

Cover design by Caroline Grimshaw
Cover illustration by Andrew Hamilton
Series design by Neil Adams
Illustrations by Bethan Matthews, Jeffrey Reid, Lisa Williams, Mel Sharp, Rhiannon Powell.

Printed by Martins the Printers, Berwick on Tweed

Contents

Introduction

Maths Call is a series of seven books from Reception to Year 6 which is designed to assist children to practise and consolidate objectives from the National Numeracy Strategy (NNS) *Framework for Teaching Mathematics* at the same time as developing their listening skills.

Listening and following instructions are two key skills that are crucial to the success of every child and every adult. How many times have children had to redo work because they have not listened to your directions? How many times do you have to repeat yourself? How often have you wished you could take time out from the overburdened curriculum to help children develop their listening skills? This series will help you solve these problems. You will not have to take time away from other curriculum areas to do this since *Maths Call* helps to develop children's listening skills and ability to follow oral directions while they practise valuable mathematical skills.

Listening and communicating

The purpose of this book is the development of children's listening skills through the mathematics curriculum, but this skill is not seen in isolation. Many of the activities outlined include reading, speaking and writing. Listening is an integral part of communication which deals with the process of giving and receiving information. The four different aspects of the communication process outlined below rely upon each other for effective communication at the same time as actively supporting and enriching one another.

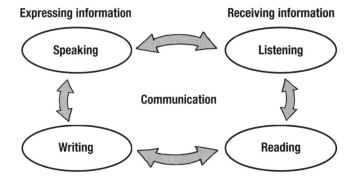

Communication and mental imagery

All children, whatever their age and ability, have their own mental images, developed from previous knowledge and experiences. Aural stimulus enables children to manipulate the mental images they have of numbers, shapes and measures. Instant recall of number facts such as the multiplication tables and the addition and subtraction number facts often depends on an aural input. Children have to hear the sounds in order to give an automatic response.

The difficult part for the teacher is to discover what is going on inside children's heads. This is where discussion as an accompaniment to mental work is so important. It is only through discussion that the teacher can begin to develop an insight into children's mental processes. Discussions also enable children to develop their own insights into their mental imagery and provide the opportunity for them to share their ideas and methods. They can form judgements about the alternatives, decide which methods are the most efficient and effective for them, and further develop flexibility and familiarity with the different mathematical topics.

The skills of listening

Listening skills can be improved through training and practice. When direct attention is paid to listening for specific purposes, and these skills are practised and consolidated, improvement in ability follows. In general children tend to learn and remember more through listening than in almost any other way. A high percentage of all the information children receive comes through their ears. Thus direct training in the skills of listening can be hugely beneficial to all learning.

Effective listening involves:
- hearing
- concentrating
- a knowledge of language
- a knowledge of the structure of language
- recognising cues
- being able to contextualise
- inferring
- thinking
- processing
- summarising
- selecting
- organising
- drawing upon previous knowledge and experience
- comprehending/understanding the main idea.

Becoming a good listener

Display the poster on page 6 to remind children of how to become a good listener. When concentrating on developing children's listening skills draw attention to the poster.

Characteristics of a good listener

A good listener is one who:
- knows how to listen
- is able to concentrate on listening
- looks at the speaker
- is courteous to the speaker
- does not interrupt the speaker
- is able to zero in on the speaker and eliminate extraneous noises and interruptions
- can comprehend
- is selective
- asks him/herself questions while listening
- draws upon their previous knowledge and experiences
- evaluates while listening
- remembers what is said
- anticipates what is coming next.

Good listening

Sit still

Think about the words

Look at the speaker

Maths Call and the teaching–learning cycle

Assessment
- Each activity can be used to assess a specific objective from the NNS *Framework*.
- Guidance given on how to record pupil performance.

Planning
- Each activity linked to an objective in the NNS *Framework*.
- Guidance given for planning a programme of work.

Teaching
- Clear and complete instructions given for each activity.
- Ideally suited to the daily mathematics lesson.

Curriculum information

Each of the 30 activities is organised under specific objectives as identified in the NNS *Framework*. The *Maths Call* objectives coverage chart on page 8 shows which activity is matched to which objective(s).

Planning a programme of work for *Maths Call*

The *Maths Call* programme chart on page 9 may be used in conjunction with your long- and medium-term plans to develop a *Maths Call* programme of work throughout the year. By following the topics allocated using the NNS *Framework* or a similar scheme of work you will ensure that the children have the opportunity to practise and consolidate the topic and specific objectives for a particular week, at the same time as developing their listening skills.

Maths Call and the daily mathematics lesson

The activities contained in *Maths Call* are ideally suited to the daily mathematics lesson. Each activity is designed to be presented to the whole class. The activities are extremely flexible and can be used in a variety of ways. For example, activities can be used during the:
- oral work and mental calculation session to practise and consolidate previously taught concepts;
- main teaching part of the lesson to focus on particular skills and concepts;
- plenary session to consolidate the concept(s) taught during the main part of the lesson and to conclude the lesson in an enjoyable way.

Maths Call objectives coverage

STRAND	TOPIC	OBJECTIVES	ACTIVITY	PAGE
Numbers and the number system	Counting and properties of numbers	Count reliably at least 20 objects.	1	12
		Count on and back in ones and tens from any small number.	2	14
		Recognise odd and even numbers.	3	16
	Place value and ordering	Read and write numbers from 0 to at least 20 in figures and words.	4	18
		Order numbers from 0 to at least 20.	5	20
		Know what each digit in a two-digit number represents. Partition two-digit numbers into a multiple of 10 and ones.	6	22
		Compare two familiar numbers. Say which is more or less and give a number which lies between them.	7	24
		Within the range 0 to 30, say the number that is 1 or 10 more or less than any given number.	8	26
		Use the vocabulary of comparing and ordering numbers in practical contexts, including ordinal numbers to at least 20.	9	28
Calculations	Addition	Recognise that more than two numbers can be added together.	10	30
		Know by heart addition facts up to 5.	11	32
		Know by heart all pairs of numbers with a total of 10.	12	34
		Use known number facts and place value to add mentally.	13	36
	Subtraction	Know by heart subtraction facts up to 5.	14	38
		Use known number facts and place value to subtract mentally.	15	40
	Addition and subtraction	Know by heart addition and subtraction facts up to 5.	16	42
		Use known number facts and place value to add and subtract mentally.	17	44
Solving problems	Reasoning about numbers	Solve simple mathematical problems or puzzles involving numbers.	18	46
	Reasoning about shapes	Solve simple mathematical problems or puzzles involving shapes.	19	48
	Problems involving 'real life'	Use mental strategies to solve simple problems set in 'real life', using counting, addition, subtraction, doubling and halving, explaining methods and reasoning orally.	20	50
	Problems involving money	Recognise coins of different values. Find totals and change.	21	52
Measures, shape and space	Measures	Understand and use the vocabulary related to length. Compare two lengths by direct comparison; extend to more than two.	22	54
		Understand and use the vocabulary related to mass. Compare two masses by direct comparison; extend to more than two.	23	56
		Understand and use the vocabulary related to capacity. Compare two capacities by direct comparison; extend to more than two.	24	58
		Understand and use the vocabulary related to time. Order familiar events in time.	25	60
		Understand and use the vocabulary related to time. Know the days of the week and the seasons of the year.	26	62
		Understand and use the vocabulary related to time. Read the time to the hour or half hour on analogue clocks.	27	64
	Shape and space	Use everyday language to describe features of common 2-D shapes.	28	66
		Use everyday language to describe features of common 3-D shapes.	29	68
		Use everyday language to describe position, direction and movement.	30	70

Maths Call programme

YEAR
CLASS
TEACHER

	WEEK	TOPIC	*MATHS CALL* ACTIVITY
AUTUMN	1		
	2		
	3		
	4		
	5		
	6		
	7		
	8		
	9		
	10		
	11		
	12		
SPRING	1		
	2		
	3		
	4		
	5		
	6		
	7		
	8		
	9		
	10		
	11		
	12		
SUMMER	1		
	2		
	3		
	4		
	5		
	6		
	7		
	8		
	9		
	10		
	11		
	12		

How to use *Maths Call*

Preparation
- Provide each child with the necessary resources. These can be found at the beginning of each activity's teacher's page.

Instructions
Explain the following to the children:
- They need to listen carefully.
- They will be given some oral instructions to follow.
- The instructions will only be given once.
- They must only do what they are told to do, nothing more.
- They may not use an eraser.
- How many instructions there are for the particular activity.
- That they are to do each task immediately after the instructions for that part have been given.

The activity
- If necessary, briefly discuss the pupil sheet with the children. Ensure that the children are familiar with the pictures and/or the text on the sheet.
- Ensure that the children are also familiar with any of the terms used in the oral instructions. Refer to the *Key words* for a list of the relevant vocabulary.
- Ask the children to write the date on the sheet in the space provided.
- Do not ask the children to write their name. This will occur during the activity.
- Slowly read through the instructions to the children.

Discussion
- After the children have completed the sheet, discuss the activity with the class. You may decide to do this either before or after marking the activity. Use the *Discussion questions* as a springboard. For each activity there are questions that have been designed to cater for higher attaining (↑) and lower attaining (↓) pupils.

Marking
- Mark the sheet with the whole class, either before or after the discussion. You may wish the children to mark their own sheet or to swap with someone next to them. However, if you are using the activity as an assessment tool then you may decide to mark the sheets yourself at a later stage.

Revisiting an activity
- Repeat an activity with the class at a later stage in the year. Children can compare how they performed on the task the second time round.
- You may like to alter the activity slightly by changing one or two of the instructions.

Maths Call and assessment

Maths Call activities may be used with the whole class or with groups of children as an assessment activity. Linked to the topic that is being studied at present, *Maths Call* will provide you with an indication of how well the children have understood the objectives being covered as well as how their listening skills are developing. The *Maths Call* assessment sheet on page 11 may be used to record how well the children have understood the objectives covered in the activity.

Maths Call assessment sheet

YEAR
CLASS
TEACHER

/ Not understood   ∠ Developing an understanding   △ Completely understood

NAME	ACTIVITY																													
	1	2	3	4	5	6	7	8	9	10	11	12	13	14	15	16	17	18	19	20	21	22	23	24	25	26	27	28	29	30

Year 1 Numbers and the number system

Counting and properties of numbers
■ Count reliably at least 20 objects.

<table>
<tr><td>

Resources

Provide each child with the following:
■ a copy of Activity 1 pupil sheet
■ a pencil

Key words

how many?　zero, one, two…twenty

</td><td>

Say to the children:

Listen carefully.

I am going to tell you some things to do.

I will say them only once, so listen very carefully.

Do only the things you are told to do and nothing else.

If you make a mistake, cross it out. Do not use an eraser.

There are 8 parts to this activity.

</td></tr>
</table>

The activity

1. Look at the branch of the tree. How many ladybirds are on the branch? Write that number under the branch.

2. Look at the ladybirds walking along the ground. How many ladybirds are there? Write that number next to the ladybirds.

3. Look at the leaf. How many ladybirds are on the leaf? Write that number under the leaf.

4. Look at the ladybird on the flower. How many dots are there on the ladybird? Write that number next to the flower.

5. Write your name under the date.

6. Look at all the ladybirds on the branch again. How many dots are there altogether on all these ladybirds? Write that number on the garden fountain.

7. Look at all the ladybirds on the ground again. How many dots are there altogether on all these ladybirds? Write that number next to the bird house.

8. Look at all the ladybirds on the leaf and on the branch. How many dots are there altogether on all the ladybirds on the leaf and branch? Write that number on the garden seat.

Answers

Discussion questions

↓ How many ladybirds are on the branch? (2)

↓ Where are there three ladybirds? (on the leaf)

■ Look at all the ladybirds on the ground. How many dots are there altogether on all these ladybirds? (15)

■ Look at all the ladybirds on the flower and the branch. How many ladybirds are there altogether? (3) How many dots are there altogether? (16)

↑ Are there more ladybirds on the ground or on the leaf? (the ground) How many more? (1)

↑ How many ladybirds are there altogether on the sheet? (10) How many dots are there altogether? (44)

Counting and properties of numbers

■ Count reliably at least 20 objects.

Date _____

Counting and properties of numbers
■ Count on and back in ones and tens from any small number.

<table>
<tr><td>

Resources

Provide each child with the following:
- ■ a copy of Activity 2 pupil sheet
- ■ a pencil

Key words

zero, one, two…one hundred   count   next

</td><td>

Say to the children:

Listen carefully.

I am going to tell you some things to do.

I will say them only once, so listen very carefully.

Do only the things you are told to do and nothing else.

If you make a mistake, cross it out. Do not use an eraser.

There are 10 parts to this activity.

</td></tr>
</table>

The activity

1. Listen carefully as I count. One, two, three, four, five.
   What number comes next? Write that number on the car.

2. Seven, eight, nine, ten, eleven. What number comes next?
   Write that number on the boat.

3. Fifteen, sixteen, seventeen, eighteen. What number comes next?
   Write that number on the bus.

4. Thirteen, twelve, eleven, ten, nine. What number comes next?
   Write that number on the train.

5. Six, five, four, three, two. What number comes next?
   Write that number on the aeroplane.

6. Ten, twenty, thirty, forty, fifty. What number comes next?
   Write that number next to the bicycle.

7. Fifty, sixty, seventy, eighty. What number comes next?
   Write that number on the truck.

8. Write your name on the scooter.

9. Ninety, eighty, seventy, sixty. What number comes next?
   Write that number on the parachute.

10. Fifty, forty, thirty, twenty. What number comes next?
    Write that number on the motorbike.

Answers

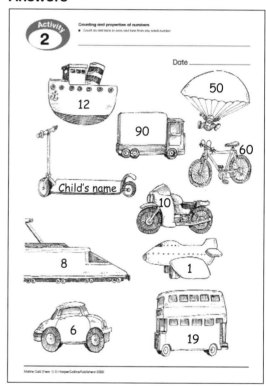

Discussion questions

↓ Look at the picture of the aeroplane. What number did you write on it? (1)

↓ What did you write on the parachute? (50)

■ Ten, twenty, thirty, forty, fifty. What number comes next? (60)
Where did you write the number sixty? (next to the bicycle)

■ What is the largest number you have written on the sheet? (90) What is the smallest number? (1)

↑ What number did you write on the train? (8) Use that number in a number pattern.

↑ Listen to this pattern. Two, four, six, eight, ten. Continue this pattern. (12, 14, 16…)

Counting and properties of numbers

■ Count on and back in ones and tens from any small number.

Date _____

Counting and properties of numbers

■ Recognise odd and even numbers.

Resources

Provide each child with the following:
■ a copy of Activity 3 pupil sheet
■ a red, blue, green and yellow coloured pencil or crayon

Key words

zero, one, two…twelve   odd   even   numbers

Say to the children:

Listen carefully.

I am going to tell you some things to do.

I will say them only once, so listen very carefully.

Do only the things you are told to do and nothing else.

If you make a mistake, cross it out. Do not use an eraser.

There are 8 parts to this activity.

The activity

This sheet shows the plan of a theatre. The letters A, B, C, D and E tell us the rows and the numbers one, two, three, four and so on tell us the seat number.

1. Look at Row A. Colour all the even numbered seats red.

2. Look at Row B. Colour all the odd numbered seats blue.

3. Look at Row B again. Colour all the even numbered seats green.

4. Look at Row C. Colour all the odd numbered seats yellow.

5. Look at Row C again. Colour all the even numbered seats red.

6. Write your name on the stage.

7. Look at Row D. Colour all the odd numbered seats blue.

8. Look at Row E. Colour all the even numbered seats green.

Answers

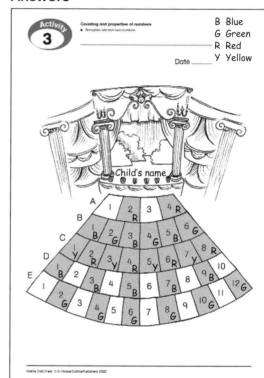

Discussion questions

↓ Look at Row A. What numbers did you colour? (2 and 4)
What do we call these numbers? (even numbers)

↓ Look at Row B. What was the first number you coloured blue? (1)
Is one an odd or an even number? (odd)

■ How many numbers did you colour in Row D? (5) What were they? (1, 3, 5, 7, 9)
What do we call these numbers? (odd numbers)

■ Look at Row C. What do you notice about the pattern you have made?
(The colours alternate yellow, red.)

↑ Look at Row D. Give me any number that lies between four and nine? (5–8 inclusive)
Is that number odd or even?

↑ Look at Row E. What do we call the numbers that you coloured? (even numbers)
Who can continue the pattern? (14, 16, 18, 20…)

Counting and properties of numbers
■ Recognise odd and even numbers.

Date _____

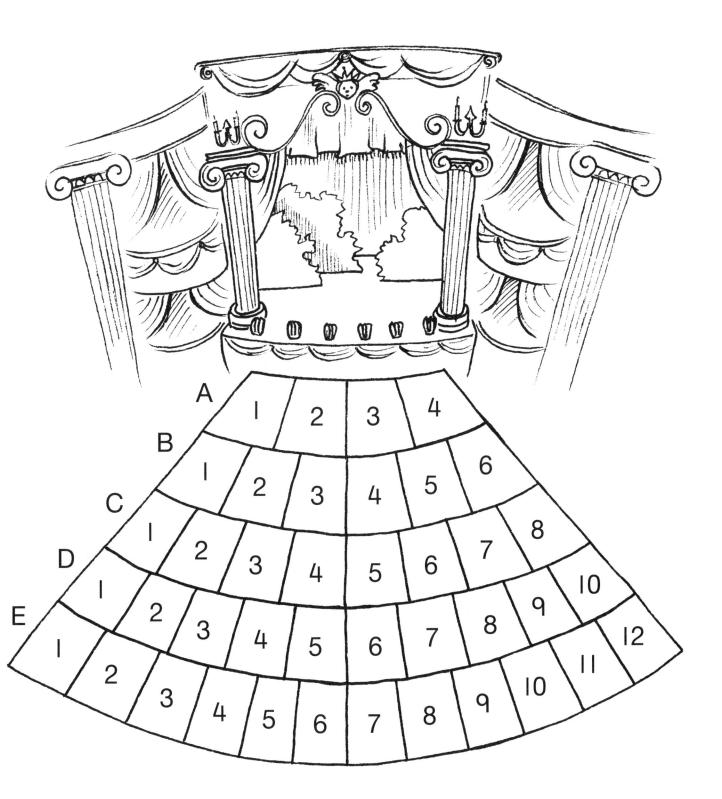

Year 1 Numbers and the number system

Place value and ordering
- Read and write numbers from 0 to at least 20 in figures and words.

Resources
Provide each child with the following:
- a copy of Activity 4 pupil sheet
- a red, blue, green and yellow coloured pencil or crayon

Key words
zero, one, two…twenty   number   word

Say to the children:
Listen carefully.
I am going to tell you some things to do.
I will say them only once, so listen very carefully.
Do only the things you are told to do and nothing else.
If you make a mistake, cross it out. Do not use an eraser.
There are 10 parts to this activity.

The activity

1. Find the number fourteen. Colour the number fourteen red.

2. Find the word fourteen. Colour the word fourteen red.

3. Find the number three. Colour the number three blue.

4. Find the word three. Colour the word three blue.

5. Write your name on the bowl.

6. Find the number nine. Colour the number nine green.

7. Find the word nine. Colour the word nine green.

8. Find the number eleven. Colour the number eleven yellow.

9. Find the word eleven. Colour the word eleven yellow.

10. Find the number seventeen. Find the word seventeen.
    Draw a ring around the number and word seventeen.

Answers

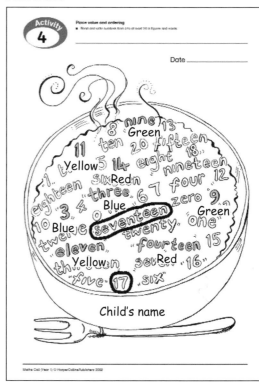

Discussion questions

↓ Tell me any number on the sheet that you coloured. (3, 9, 11 or 14)

↓ What number did you colour blue? (3)

■ Show me twelve written as a number. Show me twelve written as a word.

■ (*Point to a number/word.*) What number/word is this?

↑ Come to the board and write the number eighteen as a number and as a word.
  (18, eighteen)

↑ Come to the board and write a number that is not on the sheet. Can you write it
  as a word?

Activity 4

Place value and ordering

■ Read and write numbers from 0 to at least 20 in figures and words.

Date _____

Place value and ordering
■ Order numbers from 0 to at least 20.

Resources
Provide each child with the following:
■ a copy of Activity 5 pupil sheet
■ a pencil

Key words
zero, one, two…twenty   number track   number line

Say to the children:

Listen carefully.

I am going to tell you some things to do.

I will say them only once, so listen very carefully.

Do only the things you are told to do and nothing else.

If you make a mistake, cross it out. Do not use an eraser.

There are 11 parts to this activity.

The activity

1. Look at the number track beside the dog.
Write the number six in the correct place on the
number track.

2. Look at the number track beside the dog again.
Write the number thirteen in the correct place
on the number track.

3. Look at the number track beside the mouse.
Write the number two in the correct place on the
number track.

4. Look at the number track beside the mouse again.
Write the number sixteen in the correct place on
the number track.

5. Look at the number line beside the bird. Write the
number nine in the correct place on the number line.

6. Look at the number line beside the bird again.
Write the number eighteen in the correct place on
the number line.

7. Look at the number line beside the cat. Write the
number four in the correct place on the number line.

8. Look at the number line beside the cat again.
Write the number eleven in the correct place on
the number line.

9. Look at the number line beside the rabbit.
Write the number seven in the correct place on
the number line.

10. Look at the number line beside the rabbit again.
Write the number fifteen in the correct place on
the number line.

11. Write your name at the top of the sheet.

Answers

Child's name

Activity 5

Place value and ordering
■ Order numbers from 0 to at least 20.

Date _____

Dog: 0 | | | | | | 6 | | | 10 | | 13 | | | | | | 20

Mouse: 0 | 2 | | | | | | 10 | | | | | 16 | | | 20

Bird: 0 ... 9 10 ... 18 20

Cat: 0 ... 4 ... 11 ... 20

Rabbit: 0 ... 7 ... 15 ...

Maths Club (Year 1) © HarperCollins Publishers 2002

Discussion questions

↓ Which animal is beside the number line where you wrote the
numbers four and eleven? (the cat)

↓ Count on past twenty. (21, 22, 23, 24…)

■ What was the largest number you wrote on the number line? (18)
Which animal is beside that number line? (the bird)

■ Look at the number track beside the dog.
What numbers did you write on the number track? (6 and 13)

↑ Look at the number line beside the rabbit.
What numbers did you write on the number line? (7 and 15)
What numbers come between seven and fifteen? (8–14 inclusive)

↑ Listen carefully to these numbers. Nine, fourteen and five.
Tell me these numbers in order smallest to largest. (5, 9, 14)
What about largest to smallest? (14, 9, 5)

Place value and ordering

■ Order numbers from 0 to at least 20.

Date _____

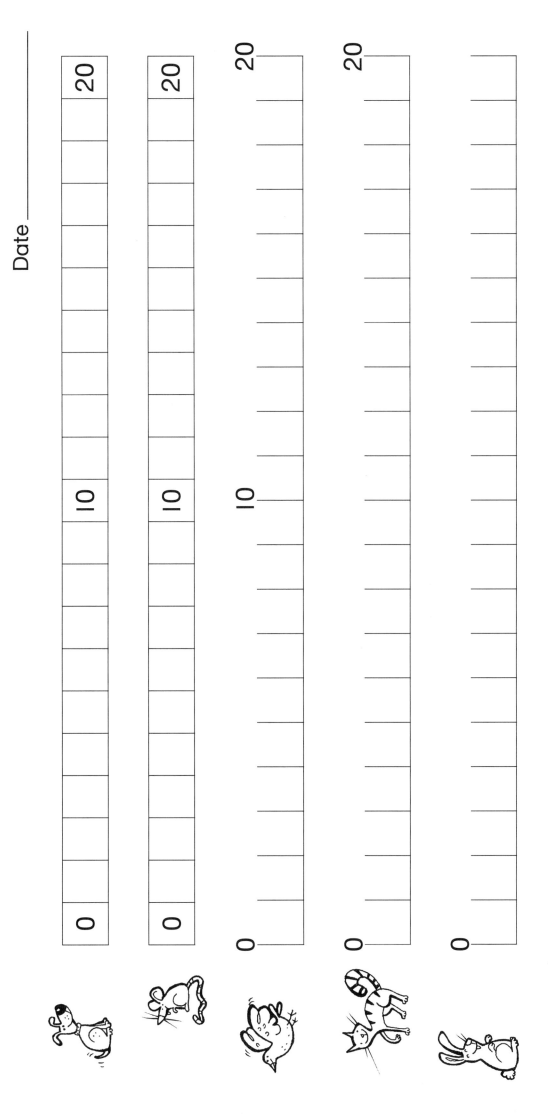

Activity 6

Place value and ordering
- Know what each digit in a two-digit number represents.
- Partition two-digit numbers into a multiple of 10 and ones.

Resources
Provide each child with the following:
- a copy of Activity 6 pupil sheet
- a red, blue, green and yellow coloured pencil or crayon
- a pencil

Key words
zero, one, two…fifty   units/ones   tens

Say to the children:

Listen carefully.

I am going to tell you some things to do.

I will say them only once, so listen very carefully.

Do only the things you are told to do and nothing else.

If you make a mistake, cross it out. Do not use an eraser.

There are 8 parts to this activity.

The activity

1. Look at the trays of blocks. Find the tray that is showing the number eighteen. Write eighteen on that tray.

2. Find the tray that is showing the number fifteen. Write fifteen on that tray.

3. Find the tray that is showing the number fourteen. Write fourteen on that tray.

4. Which tray has three tens and two units? Colour that tray blue.

5. Which tray has two tens and six units? Colour that tray green.

6. Which tray has two tens and no units? Colour that tray red.

7. Which tray is showing the number thirty-nine? Colour that tray yellow.

8. Which tray is showing the number twenty-one? Write your name on that tray.

Discussion questions

↓ Which tray did you colour red? (the tray with 20 cubes)
Write the number twenty on the board.

↓ Look at the number fifteen. How many tens are there in fifteen? (1)
How many units are there in fifteen? (5)

■ In which tray did you write your name? (the tray with 21 cubes) How many tens are there in twenty-one? (2) How many units are there in twenty-one? (1)

■ Look at the number eighteen. What does the one digit stand for? (1 ten or 10)
What does the digit eight stand for? (8 units or 8 ones)

↑ Which tray has the same number of tens and units? (22)

↑ Look at the last tray. What number does that tray show? (43)
How many tens are there in forty-three? (4) How many units? (3)
Write the number forty-three on the board.
Can you write it as a word?

Answers

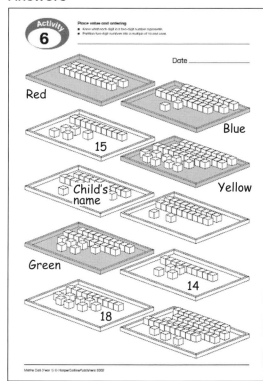

Place value and ordering

■ Know what each digit in a two-digit number represents.
■ Partition two-digit numbers into a multiple of 10 and ones.

Date _____

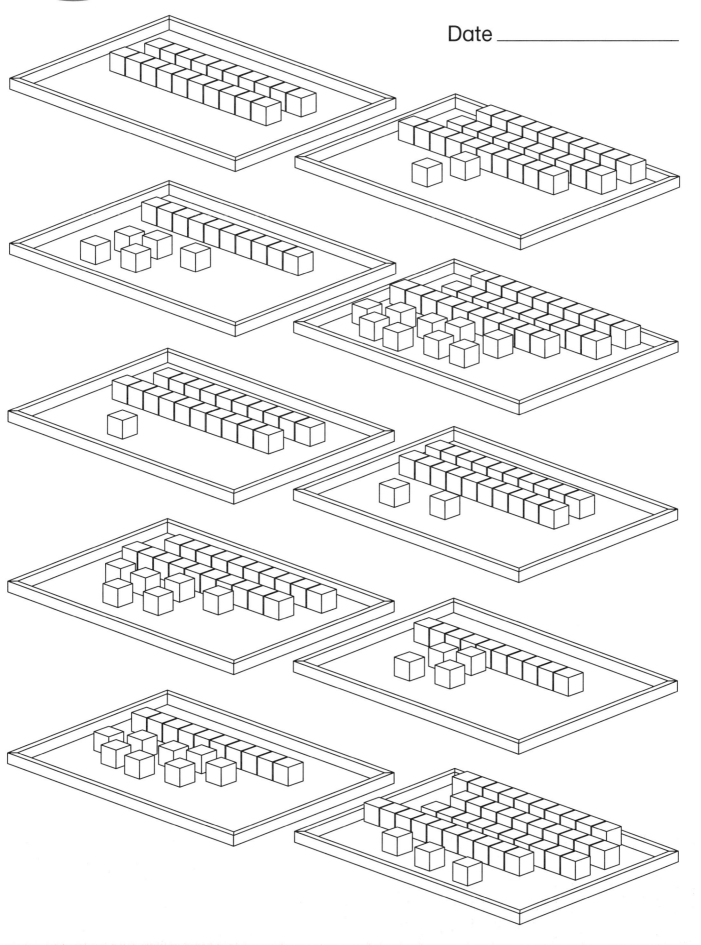

Year 1 Numbers and the number system

Place value and ordering
- Compare two familiar numbers.
- Say which is more or less and give a number which lies between them.

Resources

Provide each child with the following:
- a copy of Activity 7 pupil sheet
- a red, blue, green and yellow coloured pencil or crayon

Key words

zero, one, two…twenty-one   more   less   between

Say to the children:

Listen carefully.

I am going to tell you some things to do.

I will say them only once, so listen very carefully.

Do only the things you are told to do and nothing else.

If you make a mistake, cross it out. Do not use an eraser.

There are 9 parts to this activity.

The activity

1. Think of the numbers six and eight. Which is more? Find that number and colour it red.

2. Think of the numbers three and five. Find the number that lies between three and five and draw a red ring around it.

3. Think of the numbers nine and eleven. Which is less? Find that number and colour it blue.

4. Think of the numbers two and four. Find the number that lies between two and four and draw a blue ring around it.

5. Think of the numbers fifteen and twelve. Which is more? Find that number and colour it green.

6. Think of the numbers seventeen and twenty. Find any number that lies between seventeen and twenty and draw a green ring around it.

7. Think of the numbers twenty-one and seventeen. Which is less? Find that number and colour it yellow.

8. Think of the numbers twenty-five and twenty. Find any number that lies between twenty-five and twenty and draw a yellow ring around it.

9. Look at the number with a red circle drawn around it. Find any number that is less than that number and write your name under it.

Answers

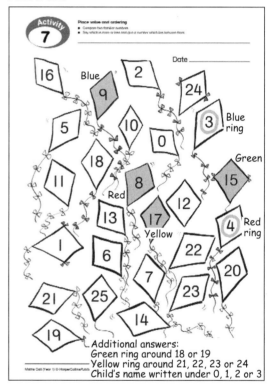

Additional answers:
Green ring around 18 or 19
Yellow ring around 21, 22, 23 or 24
Child's name written under 0, 1, 2 or 3

Discussion questions

↓ Which number did you colour yellow? (17)

↓ Look at the numbers with a blue and red ring drawn around them. Which is more? (4) Which is less? (3)

■ Look at the number that is coloured red. Tell me a number that is more than that number. (any number more than 8) Tell me a number that is less than that number. (any number less than 8)

■ Look at the numbers coloured yellow and green. What is the number that lies between them? (16)

↑ Think of the numbers twenty-four and twenty-seven. Which is less? (24) Which is more? (27)

↑ Think of the numbers twenty-six and thirty. Tell me a number between twenty-six and thirty. (27, 28 or 29)

Place value and ordering
- Compare two familiar numbers.
- Say which is more or less and give a number which lies between them.

Date _____

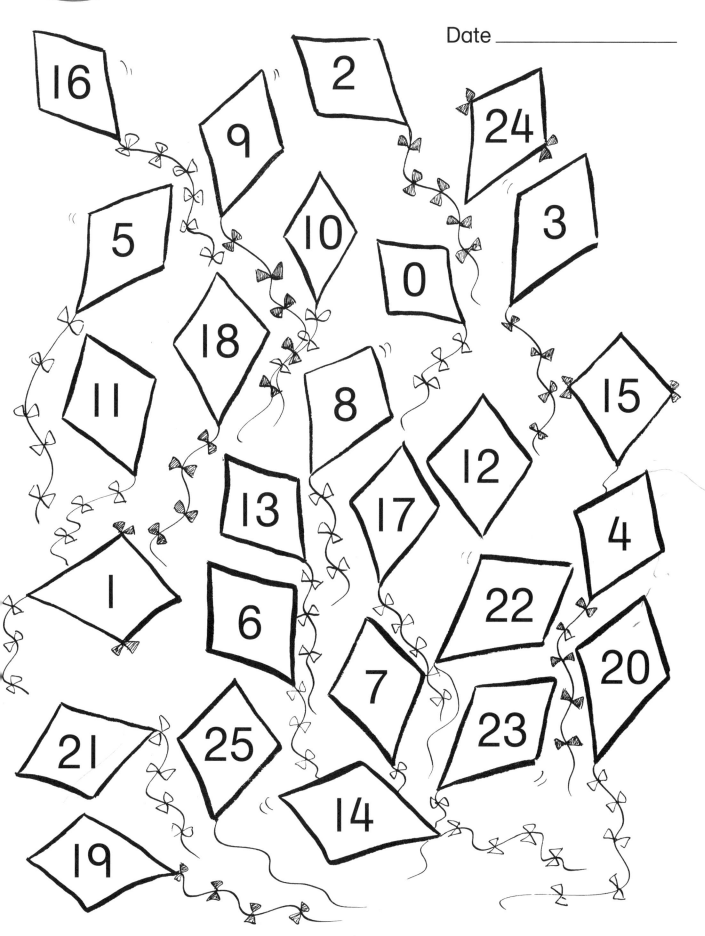

Place value and ordering

■ Within the range 0 to 30, say the number that is 1 or 10 more or less than any given number.

Resources

Provide each child with the following:
■ a copy of Activity 8 pupil sheet
■ a red, blue, green and yellow coloured pencil or crayon
■ a pencil

Key words

zero, one, two…thirty   more   less

Say to the children:

Listen carefully.

I am going to tell you some things to do.

I will say them only once, so listen very carefully.

Do only the things you are told to do and nothing else.

If you make a mistake, cross it out. Do not use an eraser.

There are 8 parts to this activity.

The activity

1. Find the number one more than seventeen. Colour that ball red.

2. Find the number one more than twenty-five. Colour that ball blue.

3. Find the number one less than twelve. Write your name above that ball.

4. Find the number one less than twenty-four. Draw a cross through that ball.

5. Find the number ten more than six. Colour that ball green.

6. Find the number ten more than seventeen. Draw a ring around that ball.

7. Find the number ten less than fourteen. Colour that ball yellow.

8. Find the number ten less than twenty-nine. Colour that ball with your lead pencil.

Discussion questions

↓ Which ball did you colour blue? (26)

↓ What number is one more than seventeen? (18)
What did you do to that ball? (coloured it red)

■ What did you do to the number that is one less than twenty-four?
(drew a cross through the number) What number was that? (23)

■ Tell me any two-digit number on the sheet. What is one more than your number?
What is one less than your number? What is ten more than your number?
What is ten less than your number?

↑ Look at the balls you coloured blue and green. What numbers are they? (26 and 16)
What can you tell me about these two numbers? (e.g. 26 is 10 more than 16; 16 is ten less than 26)

↑ Look at the ball you coloured with your lead pencil. What number is this? (19) What is ten more than 19? (29) What is ten more than 29? (39) What is ten more than 39? (49)
Can you see a pattern? (the tens digit increases by one each time)

Answers

Place value and ordering

■ Within the range 0 to 30, say the number that is 1 or 10 more or less than any given number.

Date _____

Place value and ordering

- Use the vocabulary of comparing and ordering numbers in practical contexts, including ordinal numbers to at least 20.

Resources

Provide each child with the following:
- a copy of Activity 9 pupil sheet
- a red, blue, green and yellow coloured pencil or crayon
- a pencil

Key words

first, second. third…twentieth   last   before   after

Say to the children:

Listen carefully.

I am going to tell you some things to do.

I will say them only once, so listen very carefully.

Do only the things you are told to do and nothing else.

If you make a mistake, cross it out. Do not use an eraser.

There are 10 parts to this activity.

The activity

1. Look at the bees beside the beehive. Colour the fourth bee yellow.

2. Look at the bees again. Draw a yellow ring around the second bee.

3. Look at the nuts beside the squirrel. Colour the fifth nut green.

4. Look at the nuts again. Draw a green ring around the seventh nut.

5. Look at the butterflies beside the tree. Colour the tenth butterfly red.

6. Look at the butterflies again. Draw a red ring around the last butterfly.

7. Look at the worms beside the bird. Colour the first worm blue.

8. Look at the worms again. Draw a blue ring around the thirteenth worm.

9. Look at the ants beside the ant's nest. Use your lead pencil to draw a ring round the eighteenth ant.

10. Look at the ants again. Write your name under the fourteenth ant.

Answers

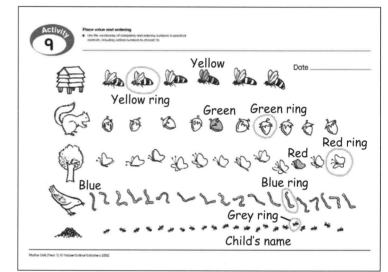

Discussion questions

↓ How many bees are there? (6)

↓ Which bee did you colour? (4th)

■ Look at the butterflies. Describe for me the butterflies that you coloured and drew a ring around? (10th and last/12th butterfly)

■ How many more ants are there than worms? (4)

↑ Look at the nut you coloured. Describe for me the position of the nuts before and after it. (4th and 6th nut)

↑ Look at the second last worm. Describe its position to me in a different way. (17th worm)

Place value and ordering

■ Use the vocabulary of comparing and ordering numbers in practical contexts, including ordinal numbers to at least 20.

Date _____

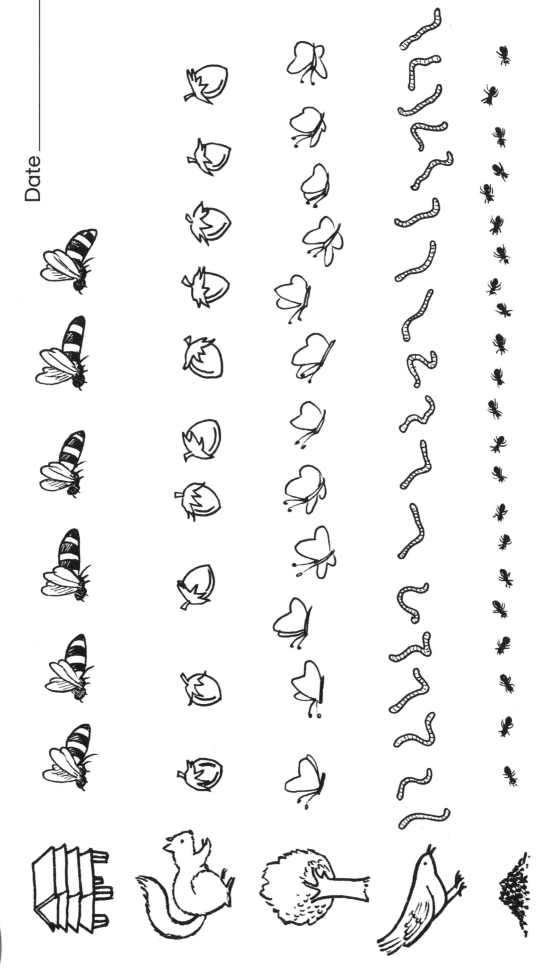

Year 1 Calculations

Addition

■ Recognise that more than two numbers can be added together.

Resources

Provide each child with the following:
■ a copy of Activity 10 pupil sheet
■ a pencil

Key words

zero, one, two…twelve   add   plus   makes   equals

Say to the children:

Listen carefully.

I am going to tell you some things to do.

I will say them only once, so listen very carefully.

Do only the things you are told to do and nothing else.

If you make a mistake, cross it out. Do not use an eraser.

There are 10 parts to this activity.

The activity

1. Look at rocket eight. Four, one and what other number make eight? Write that number on the rocket.

2. Look at rocket ten. Six, three and what other number make ten? Write that number on the rocket.

3. Look at rocket seven. Three, two and what other number equals seven? Write that number on the rocket.

4. Look at the astronaut. Write your name on the astronaut's suit.

5. Look at rocket six. Two plus one plus what other number make six? Write that number on the rocket.

6. Look at rocket twelve. Six, four and what other number equals twelve? Write that number on the rocket.

7. Look at rocket four. One add two add what other number equals four? Write that number on the rocket.

8. Look at rocket five. Two and what other two numbers make five? Write these numbers on the rocket.

9. Look at rocket nine. Write down any three numbers that, when added together, make nine.

10. Look at the last rocket. Five add two add four equals what number? Write that number on the rocket.

Answers

Discussion questions

↓ Look at rocket eight. What is four plus one? (5) Five and how many more equal eight? (3)

↓ Look at rocket four. One add two add what other number equals four? (1)

■ Look at the last rocket. What does five add two add four equal? (11)

■ Look at rocket five. Two and what other numbers make five? (1, 2)
Did anyone write anything different? (3, 0)

↑ Look at rocket nine. What are three numbers that when added together make nine? (e.g. 3, 4, 2)
Did anyone write some different numbers? (e.g. 2, 2, 5) Are there any others? (e.g. 1, 2, 6)

↑ Look at the three rockets at the top of the sheet. What is eight, add ten, add seven? (25)
How did you work it out? How else could you have worked it out? Did anyone work it out in a different way?

Addition

■ Recognise that more than two numbers can be added together.

Date _____

Addition
- Know by heart addition facts up to 5.

Resources

Provide each child with the following:
- a copy of Activity 11 pupil sheet
- a red, blue, green and yellow coloured pencil or crayon
- a pencil
- a ruler

Key words

zero, one, two…five   add   plus   makes   equals

Say to the children:

Listen carefully.

I am going to tell you some things to do.

I will say them only once, so listen very carefully.

Do only the things you are told to do and nothing else.

If you make a mistake, cross it out. Do not use an eraser.

There are 11 parts to this activity.

The activity

1. Put your lead pencil on dot number one. One plus two equals what number? Draw a line from dot one to that number.

2. One add three equals what number? Draw a green ring around that number.

3. Put your lead pencil on dot number two. Two add two makes what number? Draw a line from dot two to that number.

4. One plus zero equals what number? Draw a red ring around that number.

5. Put your lead pencil on dot number three. Three plus two equals what number? Draw a line from dot three to that number.

6. Two add one equals what number? Draw a blue ring around that number.

7. Put your lead pencil on dot number one. One plus one equals what number? Draw a line from dot one to that number.

8. Zero plus two equals what number? Draw a yellow ring around that number.

9. Put your lead pencil on dot number four. Four plus one equals what number? Draw a line from dot four to that number.

10. Two add three equals what number? Use your lead pencil to draw a ring around that number.

11. Write your name inside the star.

Answers

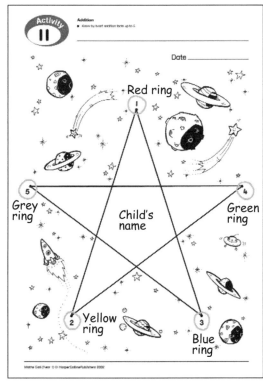

Discussion questions

↓ What is the largest number on the sheet? (5)
What is the smallest number on the sheet? (1)

↓ What is two plus two? (4)

■ Three and what other number makes five? (2)

■ Give me another sum where the answer is five. (e.g. 4 + 1)
Are there any others? (e.g. 5 + 0)

↑ Look at the numbers you drew a green and blue ring around.
What do they add up to? (7)

↑ What do all the numbers around the outside of the star add up to? (15)

Addition

■ Know by heart addition facts up to 5.

_____

Date _____

Addition

■ Know by heart all pairs of numbers with a total of 10.

Resources

Provide each child with the following:
■ a copy of Activity 12 pupil sheet
■ a red, blue, green, yellow, orange and purple coloured pencil or crayon

Key words

zero, one, two…ten   add   plus   makes   how many more?
equals

Say to the children:

Listen carefully.

I am going to tell you some things to do.

I will say them only once, so listen very carefully.

Do only the things you are told to do and nothing else.

If you make a mistake, cross it out. Do not use an eraser.

There are 13 parts to this activity.

The activity

1. Find number two. Colour it red.

2. Two add what other number makes ten? Colour that number red.

3. Find number five. Colour it blue.

4. Five add what other number equals ten? Colour that number blue.

5. Find number one. Colour it green.

6. One plus what other number equals ten? Colour that number green.

7. Find number seven. Colour it yellow.

8. Seven and what other number makes ten? Colour that number yellow.

9. Find number ten. Colour it orange.

10. Ten and how many more makes ten? Colour that number orange.

11. Find number six. Colour it purple.

12. Six add what other number equals ten? Colour that number purple.

13. Write your name at the top of the sheet.

Answers

Discussion questions

↓ What two numbers did you colour yellow? (7 and 3)
What is seven add three? (10)

↓ Tell me two other numbers that make ten. (e.g. 6 and 4)

■ Two and what other number makes ten? (8)

■ If you have five, how many more do you need to make ten? (5)

↑ If six add four equals ten, what is four add six? (10)
How do you know? (addition can be done in any order)

↑ Tell me three numbers that when added together make ten. (e.g. 2, 3 and 5)

Addition
■ Know by heart all pairs of numbers with a total of 10.

Date

Addition

■ Use known number facts and place value to add mentally.

Resources

Provide each child with the following:
■ a copy of Activity 13 pupil sheet
■ a red, blue, green, yellow, orange and purple coloured pencil or crayon

Key words

zero, one, two…twenty-five add plus double makes equals

Say to the children:

Listen carefully.

I am going to tell you some things to do.

I will say them only once, so listen very carefully.

Do only the things you are told to do and nothing else.

If you make a mistake, cross it out. Do not use an eraser.

There are 12 parts to this activity.

The activity

1. Write your name at the top of the sheet.

2. What is ten add one? Colour that patch red.

3. What is five add ten? Colour that patch red.

4. Three plus four. Colour that patch blue.

5. Ten add nine. Colour that patch green.

6. What is two plus one? Colour that patch yellow.

7. What is thirteen add four? Colour that patch green.

8. What is double four? Colour that patch orange.

9. Six plus three. Colour that patch blue.

10. Twenty add three. Colour that patch yellow.

11. What is thirteen plus five? Colour that patch orange.

12. Eleven add two. Colour that patch purple.

Answers

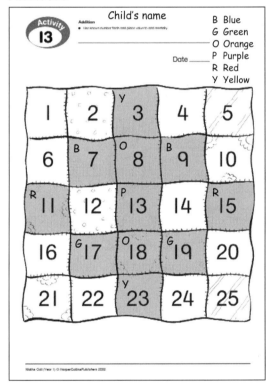

Discussion questions

↓ What is ten add nine? (19) Did you colour that number? (yes) What colour? (green)

↓ Tell me two numbers that when added together make 6. (e.g. 4 and 2)

■ Look at the two numbers you coloured green. How many more do you need to add to seventeen to make nineteen? (2)

■ Look at the two numbers you coloured red. What do these two numbers add up to? (26) How did you work this out?

↑ Look at the two numbers you coloured blue. What do these two numbers add up to? (16) How did you work it out?

↑ Give me a sum for a number you did not colour.

Addition

■ Use known number facts and place value to add mentally.

Date _____

1	2	3	4	5
6	7	8	9	10
11	12	13	14	15
16	17	18	19	20
21	22	23	24	25

Subtraction

■ Know by heart subtraction facts up to 5.

Resources

Provide each child with the following:
■ a copy of Activity 14 pupil sheet
■ a coloured pencil or crayon

Key words

zero, one, two...five   number track   subtract   minus
take away   difference   leaves   equals

Say to the children:

Listen carefully.

I am going to tell you some things to do.

I will say them only once, so listen very carefully.

Do only the things you are told to do and nothing else.

If you make a mistake, cross it out. Do not use an eraser.

There are 10 parts to this activity.

The activity

1. Look at the number track beside the apple. What is three take away one? Draw a cross through that number on the track.

2. Look at the number track beside the apple again. What is five subtract one? Draw a ring around that number on the track.

3. Look at the number track beside the orange. Four minus three. Draw a line under that number on the track.

4. Look at the number track beside the orange again. Five take away two. Write your name under that number on the track.

5. Look at the number track beside the banana. What is two subtract two? Colour that number on the track.

6. Look at the number track beside the banana again. What is five minus zero? Draw a cross through that number on the track.

7. Look at the number track beside the grapes. Five take away three. Draw a line under that number on the track.

8. Look at the number track beside the grapes again. What is four minus one? Draw a ring around that number on the track.

9. Look at the number track beside the pear. Three subtract two. Colour that number on the track.

10. Look at the number track beside the pear again. What is the difference between four and zero? Draw a cross through that number on the track.

Answers

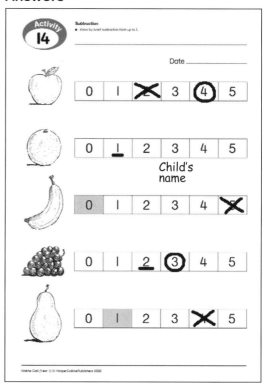

Discussion questions

⬇ What is three subtract one? (2) You can use the number track to help you if you need to.

⬇ What is the largest number you drew a cross through? (5)
What is the smallest number you drew a cross through? (2)

■ What is another word for take away? (minus, subtract, difference)

■ Look at the two numbers you drew a ring around. What is the difference between these two numbers? (1)

⬆ Five take away how many leaves you with three? (2)
How did you work it out? Did anyone work it out a different way?

⬆ What number when you take away one leaves you with three? (4)

Subtraction

■ Know by heart subtraction facts up to 5.

Date _____

0	1	2	3	4	5

0	1	2	3	4	5

0	1	2	3	4	5

0	1	2	3	4	5

0	1	2	3	4	5

Activity 15

Subtraction

■ Use known number facts and place value to subtract mentally.

Resources

Provide each child with the following:
■ a copy of Activity 15 pupil sheet
■ a red, blue, green, yellow, orange and purple coloured pencil or crayon

Key words

zero, one, two…twenty-one   subtract   minus   take away
difference   leaves   equals

Say to the children:

Listen carefully.

I am going to tell you some things to do.

I will say them only once, so listen very carefully.

Do only the things you are told to do and nothing else.

If you make a mistake, cross it out. Do not use an eraser.

There are 10 parts to this activity.

The activity

1. What is eight subtract five? Colour that ice-cream red.

2. What is ten subtract four? Colour that ice-cream blue.

3. Seven minus three. Colour that ice-cream green.

4. Ten minus one. Colour that ice-cream blue.

5. What is the difference between sixteen and three? Colour that ice-cream red.

6. Write your name on the ice-cream van.

7. What is fifteen take away four? Colour that ice-cream green.

8. Twenty minus five. Colour that ice-cream orange.

9. What is eighteen take away six? Colour that ice-cream yellow.

10. What is the difference between twenty and three? Colour that ice-cream purple.

Discussion questions

↓ What is ten subtract one? (9) What colour did you colour that number? (blue)

↓ Look at the two numbers that are coloured blue. What are they? (6 and 9)
What is nine take away six? (3)

■ Look at the two numbers that are coloured red. What is the difference between these two numbers? (10)

■ What is eighteen minus six? (12) What colour is number twelve? (yellow)

↑ Look at the two numbers that are coloured green. What is the difference between these two numbers? (7)

↑ Look at the numbers you coloured purple and yellow. What are these numbers? (17 and 12) What is the difference between these two numbers? (5)

Answers

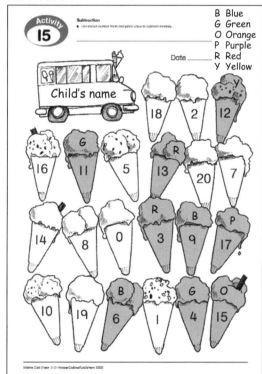

Subtraction

■ Use known number facts and place value to subtract mentally.

Date _____

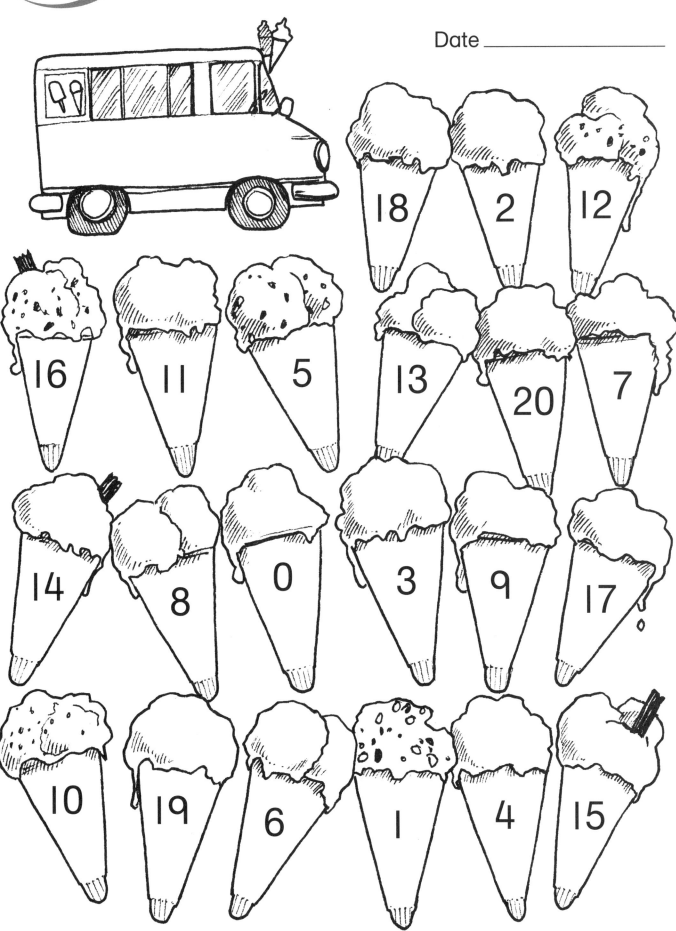

Addition and subtraction

■ Know by heart addition and subtraction facts up to 5.

<table>
<tr><td>

Resources

Provide each child with the following:
■ a copy of Activity 16 pupil sheet
■ a pencil

Key words

zero, one, two…five   number sentence   add   plus   subtract
minus   take away   difference   leaves   equals

</td><td>

Say to the children:

Listen carefully.

I am going to tell you some things to do.

I will say them only once, so listen very carefully.

Do only the things you are told to do and nothing else.

If you make a mistake, cross it out. Do not use an eraser.

There are 6 parts to this activity.

</td></tr>
</table>

The activity

1. Look at the house. Look at all the number sentences in the windows. Only write down the answers to the number sentences that have an answer of four.

2. Look at the shop. Look at all the number sentences in the windows. Only write down the answers to the number sentences that have an answer of one.

3. Look at the bus. Look at all the number sentences. Only write down the answers to the number sentences that have an answer of three.

4. Look at the aeroplane. Look at all the number sentences. Only write down the answers to the number sentences that have an answer of two.

5. Look at the school. Look at all the number sentences. Only write down the answers to the number sentences that have an answer of five.

6. Write your name on the school.

Discussion questions

↓ Look at the bus. Read out the number sentences you answered.
(2 + 1 = 3; 5 − 2 = 3; 3 + 0 = 3)

↓ Look at the shop. How many answers did you write down? (2) What were they? (1 and 1)
Read out those number sentences. (1 + 0 = 1; 5 − 4 = 1)

■ Read out the answers to the number sentences you answered in the school.
(3 + 2 = 5; 1 + 4 = 5; 5 − 0 = 5)

■ Look at the number sentences on the aeroplane. What are the answers to the number sentences you did not answer? (2 − 1 = 1; 2 − 2 = 0)

↑ Look at the house. What was the answer to the number sentences you answered? (4)
Tell me some other number sentences with an answer of four.
(e.g. 2 + 2 = 4; 4 + 0 = 4)

↑ Look at the school. Read out the number sentences you did not answer.
(4 − 1 = 3; 5 − 3 = 2)

Answers

Addition and subtraction
- Know by heart addition and subtraction facts up to 5.

Date _____

$3 - 2 = \square$ $1 + 3 = \square$

$5 - 1 = \square$ $3 + 0 = \square$

$1 + 0 = \square$ $4 - 2 = \square$

$1 + 1 = \square$ $5 - 4 = \square$

$2 + 1 = \square$ $5 - 2 = \square$

$3 + 0 = \square$ $3 - 1 = \square$

$2 + 2 = \square$

$1 + 1 = \square$ $2 - 2 = \square$ $4 - 2 = \square$ $2 + 0 = \square$

$2 - 1 = \square$ $5 - 3 = \square$

$3 + 2 = \square$ $5 - 3 = \square$ $5 - 0 = \square$

$4 - 1 = \square$

SCHOOL

$1 + 4 = \square$

Addition and subtraction

■ Use known number facts and place value to add and subtract mentally.

Resources

Provide each child with the following:
■ a copy of Activity 17 pupil sheet
■ a pencil

Key words

zero, one, two...thirty add plus double subtract minus
take away difference leaves equals

Say to the children:

Listen carefully.

I am going to tell you some things to do.

I will say them only once, so listen very carefully.

Do only the things you are told to do and nothing else.

If you make a mistake, cross it out. Do not use an eraser.

There are 14 parts to this activity.

The activity

1. Put your pencil on dot eighteen.
   Twenty plus six equals what number?
   Draw a line from dot eighteen to that number.

2. Put your pencil on dot twenty-five.
   Ten plus six makes what number?
   Draw a line from dot twenty-five to that number.

3. Put your pencil on dot twenty-nine.
   Ten subtract three equals what number?
   Draw a line from dot twenty-nine to that number.

4. Put your pencil on dot six.
   Ten take away zero is what number?
   Draw a line from dot six to that number.

5. Put your pencil on dot twenty-three.
   Four add ten makes what number? Draw a line
   from dot twenty-three to that number.

6. Put your pencil on dot twenty-two. Ten add five equals
   what number? Draw a line from dot twenty-two to that number.

7. Put your pencil on dot thirty. Ten subtract two equals
   what number? Draw a line from dot thirty to that number.

8. Put your pencil on dot eighteen. Six minus four equals
   what number? Draw a line from dot eighteen to that number.

9. Put your pencil on dot twenty-eight. Ten and five more makes
   what number? Draw a line from dot twenty-eight to that number.

10. Put your pencil on dot twenty-three. Double ten is
    what number? Draw a line from dot twenty-three to that number.

11. Put your pencil on dot ten. What is the difference between
    seven and four? Draw a line from dot ten to that number.

12. Put your pencil on dot twenty-six. Ten add three equals what
    number? Draw a line from dot twenty-six to that number.

13. Turn the sheet upside down. What have you drawn? (a boat)

14. Write your name on the boat.

Answers

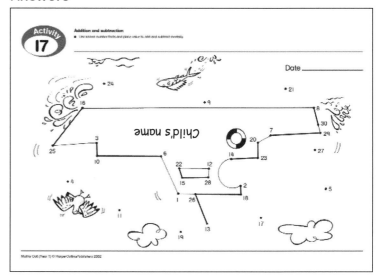

Discussion questions

↓ What is six add ten? (16)
   Did you use the number sixteen to draw the boat? (yes)

↓ What is another word for minus?
   (subtract, take away, difference)

■ What is twenty subtract six? (14)

■ Give another number sentence where the answer is
   fourteen. (e.g. 10 + 4)

↑ Look at the numbers that make up the window.
   What is fifteen add twelve? (27)
   What is the difference between twelve and fifteen? (3)

↑ Tell me a number we did not use to draw the boat.
   (4, 5, 9, 11, 17, 19, 21, 24 or 27)
   Give me a number sentence using two of these
   numbers. Can you give me another one?

Addition and subtraction

- Use known number facts and place value to add and subtract mentally.

Date _____

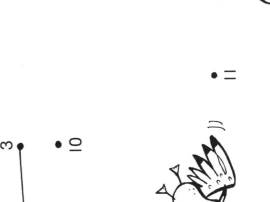

• 21

• 30   • 29

• 27

• 5

• 7

• 23

20

• 2

• 18

14

• 17

• 9

12   • 28

• 13

22   • 15

6   • 1   26

• 19

• 24

• 11

3

• 10

• 16

• 4

25

Year 1 Solving problems

Reasoning about numbers
■ Solve simple mathematical problems or puzzles involving numbers.

Say to the children:
Listen carefully.
I am going to tell you some things to do.
I will say them only once, so listen very carefully.
Do only the things you are told to do and nothing else.
If you make a mistake, cross it out. Do not use an eraser.
There are 12 parts to this activity.

The activity

1. Look at the dice. Colour any two dice that add up to six.

2. Look at the dice again. Draw a ring around any two dice that have a difference of three.

3. Look at the dominoes. Colour any two dominoes that add up to ten.

4. Look at the dominoes again. What is eight take away three?
   Draw a ring around the domino that shows that number.

5. Look at the building blocks with numbers on them. Which block shows the answer to double six? Colour that block.

6. Look at the building blocks with numbers on them again. Which block shows the answer to double five? Draw a ring around that block.

7. Look at all the building blocks. Re-arrange the blocks with numbers on them in order smallest to largest. Write the numbers in order on the empty building blocks underneath.

8. Look at the jug. Write on the jug any two numbers that add up to twelve.

9. Look at the cup. Write on the cup any two numbers that add up to seven.

10. Look at the bowl. Write on the bowl any three numbers that add up to ten.

11. Look at the vase. Write on the vase any three numbers that add up to twelve.

12. Write your name above the bowl.

Answers

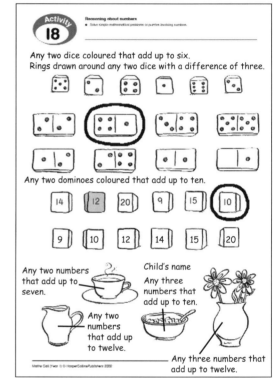

Discussion questions

↓ Which two dice add up to six? (4 and 2; 5 and 1)
Did anyone have anything different? Are there any others? (no)

↓ Look at the cup. Which two numbers add up to seven?
(e.g. 5 and 2) Did anyone have anything different?
Are there any others?

■ Look at the building blocks you wrote on. Tell me the numbers you wrote in order from smallest to largest.
(9, 10, 12, 14, 15, 20) What about from largest to smallest?
(20, 15, 14, 12, 10, 9)

■ Look at the dominoes. Which three dominoes add up to seven? (4, 2 and 1)

↑ Look at the building blocks. What is twenty add ten? (30)
Ten plus fifteen? (25) What is the difference between twelve and fifteen? (3) Fourteen subtract nine? (5)
Which block shows the answer to double seven? (14)

↑ Look at the jug. What numbers did you write down that add up to twelve? (e.g. 10 and 2; 5 and 7) Did anyone have anything different? Are there any others?

Reasoning about numbers

■ Solve simple mathematical problems or puzzles involving numbers.

Date _____

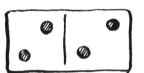   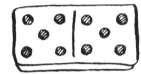

14　　12　　20　　9　　15　　10

Reasoning about shapes

■ Solve simple mathematical problems or puzzles involving shapes.

Resources

Provide each child with the following:
■ a copy of Activity 19 pupil sheet
■ a pencil

Key words

square   rectangle   triangle   circle   star   cube   cuboid
cylinder   cone   sphere   pyramid   sides   faces

Say to the children:
Listen carefully.
I am going to tell you some things to do.
I will say them only once, so listen very carefully.
Do only the things you are told to do and nothing else.
If you make a mistake, cross it out. Do not use an eraser.
There are 12 parts to this activity.

The activity

In this activity you draw a tick for 'yes' or a cross for 'no'.

1. Look at Shape A. Is it a triangle? Draw a tick inside the shape for 'yes' or a cross inside the shape for 'no'.

2. Look at Shape B. Is it a cone? Draw a tick inside the shape for 'yes' or a cross inside the shape for 'no'.

3. Look at Shape C. Is it a rectangle? Draw a tick inside the shape for 'yes' or a cross inside the shape for 'no'.

4. Look at Shape D. Is it a circle? Draw a tick inside the shape for 'yes' or a cross inside the shape for 'no'.

5. Look at Shape E. Is it a cone? Draw a tick inside the shape for 'yes' or a cross inside the shape for 'no'.

6. Find the square. Write your name inside the square.

7. Look at Shape F. Is it a cube? Draw a tick inside the shape for 'yes' or a cross inside the shape for 'no'.

8. Look at Shape G. Is it a cube? Draw a tick inside the shape for 'yes' or a cross inside the shape for 'no'.

9. Look at Shape H. Is it a star? Draw a tick inside the shape for 'yes' or a cross inside the shape for 'no'.

10. Look at Shape I. Is it a triangle? Draw a tick inside the shape for 'yes' or a cross inside the shape for 'no'.

11. Look at Shape K. Is it a cylinder? Draw a tick inside the shape for 'yes' or a cross inside the shape for 'no'.

12. Look at Shape L. Is it a sphere? Draw a tick inside the shape for 'yes' or a cross inside the shape for 'no'.

Answers

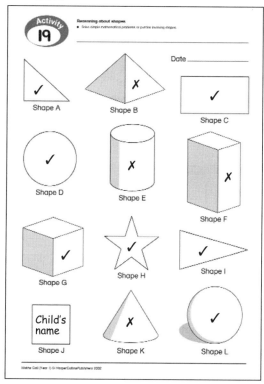

Discussion questions

↓ What is Shape A? (triangle)

↓ Is there another triangle on the page? (yes) Which shape? (Shape I)

■ Which shape is the cylinder/pyramid? (Shape E/B)

■ How many shapes have a cross in them? (4)
What shapes are they? (pyramid, cylinder, cuboid, cone)

↑ Name the 3-D shapes on the sheet. (pyramid, cylinder, cuboid, cube, cone, sphere)

↑ Do all triangles have three sides? (yes) Do all cubes have six faces? (yes)
Which other shape has six faces? (cuboid)

Reasoning about shapes

■ Solve simple mathematical problems or puzzles involving shapes.

Date _____

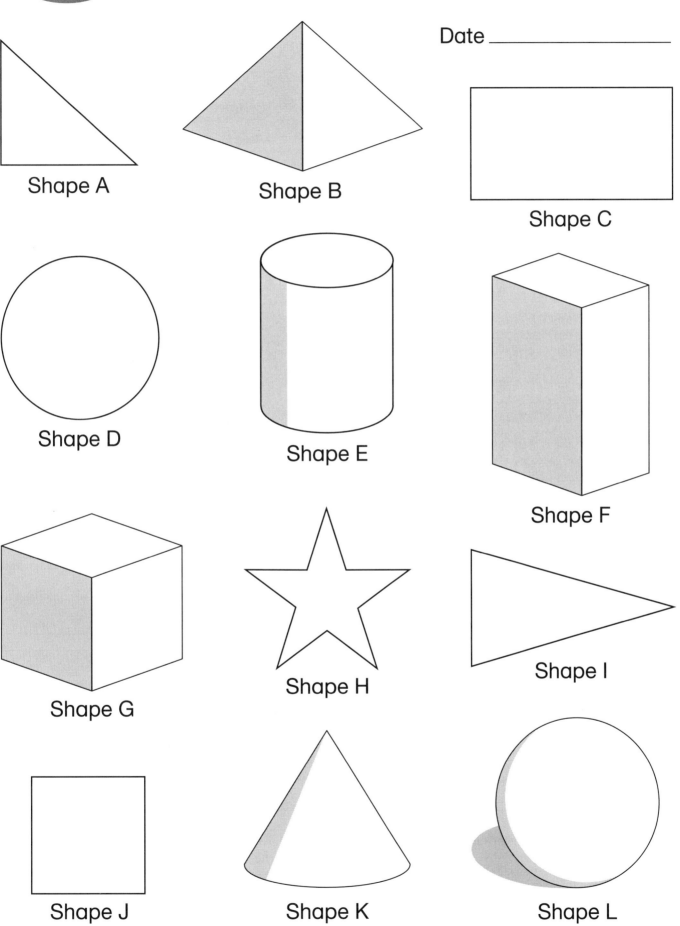

Shape A

Shape B

Shape C

Shape D

Shape E

Shape F

Shape G

Shape H

Shape I

Shape J

Shape K

Shape L

Problems involving 'real life'

■ Use mental strategies to solve simple problems set in 'real life', using counting, addition, subtraction, doubling and halving, explaining methods and reasoning orally.

Resources
Provide each child with the following:
■ a copy of Activity 20 pupil sheet
■ a pencil

Key words
altogether   how many more?

Say to the children:
Listen carefully.
I am going to tell you some things to do.
I will say them only once, so listen very carefully.
Do only the things you are told to do and nothing else.
If you make a mistake, cross it out. Do not use an eraser.
There are 9 parts to this activity.

The activity

Manor Infants are having a sports day. All the children in the school are put into four teams – Red, Blue, Green and Yellow. Your sheet shows the score cards for the two Year 1 classes – Miss Arnold's class (1A) and Mr Bryce's class (1B).

1. Look at the score card for Miss Arnold's class. How many points have the red team scored? Write that number on the bat.

2. Look at the score card for Miss Arnold's class again. How many points have the green and yellow teams scored altogether? Write that number on the ball.

3. Look at the score card for Miss Arnold's class again. How many points have the blue and green teams scored altogether? Write that number under the skipping rope.

4. Again, look at the score card for Miss Arnold's class. The green team has scored more points than the yellow team. How many more? Write that number under the finishing line.

5. Now look at the score card for Mr Bryce's class. How many points have the red and blue teams scored altogether? Write that number inside the winner's ribbon.

6. Look at the score card for Mr Bryce again. How many points have the red, green and yellow teams scored altogether? Write that number on the whistle.

7. Look at the trophy. Write your name under the trophy.

8. Again look at the score card for Mr Bryce's class. The yellow team has scored more points than the green team. How many more? Write that number near the pair of trainers.

9. Now look at the score cards for both classes. How many points have the red team won altogether? Write that number on the towel.

Answers

Discussion questions

↓ Which team in Miss Arnold's class has scored the most/least points? (red/yellow)

↓ How many points has the Green team scored altogether? (9)

■ Which team has scored thirteen points altogether? (blue)

■ How many points has Miss Arnold's class scored altogether? (23)

↑ Which class has scored the most points? (Miss Arnold's class) How did you work this out?

↑ In Year 1 which team is winning/losing? (blue/green) How did you work this out?

Problems involving 'real life'

■ Use mental strategies to solve simple problems set in 'real life', using counting, addition, subtraction, doubling and halving, explaining methods and reasoning orally.

Date _____

CLASS 1A

Team	Score
Red	9
Blue	6
Green	5
Yellow	3

CLASS 1B

Team	Score
Red	2
Blue	7
Green	4
Yellow	8

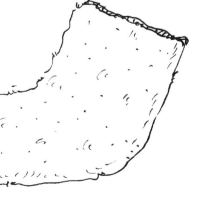

Problems involving money

- Recognise coins of different values.
- Find totals and change.

Resources

Provide each child with the following:
- a copy of Activity 21 pupil sheet
- a red, blue, green and yellow coloured pencil or crayon

Key words

coin   pence   penny   pee   pound   amount   change

Say to the children:

Listen carefully.

I am going to tell you some things to do.

I will say them only once, so listen very carefully.

Do only the things you are told to do and nothing else.

If you make a mistake, cross it out. Do not use an eraser.

There are 11 parts to this activity.

The activity

1. Look at the money at the top of the sheet. Find the fifty pence coin. Colour the fifty pence coin red.

2. Find the one penny coin. Colour the one penny coin blue.

3. Find the ten pence coin. Colour the ten pence coin green.

4. Find the twenty pence coin. Write your name under the twenty pence coin.

5. Find the one pound coin. Colour the one pound coin yellow.

6. Look at the piggy bank. How much money is in the piggy bank? Write that amount inside the piggy bank.

7. Look at the jar. How much money is in the jar? Write that amount inside the jar.

8. Look at the sock. How much money is in the sock? Write that amount inside the sock.

9. Look at the moneybox. How much money is in the moneybox? Write that amount inside the moneybox.

10. Look at the purse. How much money is in the purse? Write that amount inside the purse.

11. Look at the hand. If you had ten pence and bought a chew worth six pence, how much change would you get back? Write that amount on the hand.

Answers

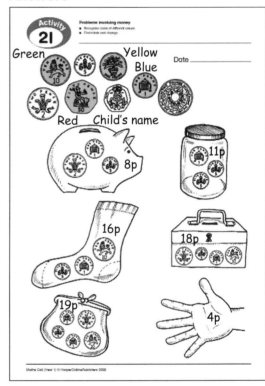

Discussion questions

↓ Which coin did you colour green? (10p coin)

↓ Describe for me the five pence coin. (e.g. the smallest silver coin)

■ How much money is inside the sock? (16p)

■ If you had ten pence and bought a chew worth six pence, how much change would you get back? (4p)

↑ Look at the money inside the piggy bank and the jar. How much money is that altogether? (19p)

↑ Look at the money inside the sock and the jar. How much more money is inside the sock? (5p)

Problems involving money
- Recognise coins of different values.
- Find totals and change.

Date _____

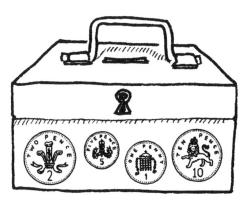

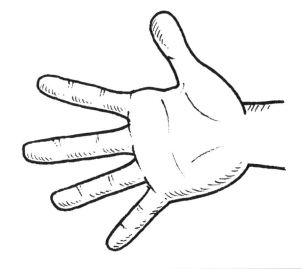

Measures

- Understand and use the vocabulary related to length.
- Compare two lengths by direct comparison; extend to more than two.

Resources

Provide each child with the following:
- a copy of Activity 22 pupil sheet
- a red, blue, green and yellow coloured pencil or crayon
- a pair of scissors

Key words

long/longer/longest   short/shorter/shortest   thick/thicker/thickest
thin/thinner/thinnest   order

Say to the children:

Listen carefully.

I am going to tell you some things to do.

I will say them only once, so listen very carefully.

Do only the things you are told to do and nothing else.

If you make a mistake, cross it out. Do not use an eraser.

There are 10 parts to this activity.

The activity

1. Look at the trains. Colour the longest train red.

2. Look at the trains again. Colour the shortest train blue.

3. Look at the trees. Write your name above the thickest tree trunk.

4. Look at the trees again. Colour the thinnest tree trunk yellow.

5. Look at the trees again. Draw four red apples on the tallest tree.

6. Again, look at the trees. Draw two green apples on the shortest tree.

7. Cut out the trains.

8. Arrange the trains in order shortest to longest.

9. Now cut out the trees.

10. Arrange the trees in order tallest to shortest.

Discussion questions

↓ Which train is the longest? (red, 8 carriages).

↓ Which tree is the tallest? (4 red apples)

■ Arrange the trees in order shortest to tallest.

■ How could you work out the length of the trains? (counting the number of carriages)
Tell me about the shortest and longest trains. (shortest train has 2 carriages, longest train
has 8 carriages)

↑ Look at the tree you coloured yellow. What can you tell me about the height of this tree?
(e.g. It is shorter than the tree with my name above it and the tree with 4 red apples on it.
It is taller than the tree with 2 green apples on it.)

↑ What is the difference in size between the longest and shortest train? (6 carriages)

Answers

Measures

- Understand and use the vocabulary related to length.
- Compare two lengths by direct comparison; extend to more than two.

Date _____

Activity 23

Measures

■ Understand and use the vocabulary related to mass.
■ Compare two masses by direct comparison; extend to more than two.

Resources

Provide each child with the following:
■ a copy of Activity 23 pupil sheet
■ a blue, green and yellow coloured pencil or crayon
■ a pair of scissors

Key words

light/lighter/lightest   heavy/heavier/heaviest   order

Say to the children:

Listen carefully.

I am going to tell you some things to do.

I will say them only once, so listen very carefully.

Do only the things you are told to do and nothing else.

If you make a mistake, cross it out. Do not use an eraser.

There are 8 parts to this activity.

The activity

1. Look at the animals. Colour the heaviest animal blue.

2. Look at the animals again. Colour the lightest animal yellow.

3. Look at the objects that you find in the kitchen.
    Colour the heaviest object green.

4. Look at the objects that you find in the kitchen again. Write your name next to the lightest object.

5. Cut out the animals.

6. Arrange the animals in order lightest to heaviest.

7. Now cut out the kitchen objects.

8. Arrange the kitchen objects in order heaviest to lightest.

Answers

Discussion questions

↓ Which is the lightest animal? (the bee)

↓ Which kitchen object is the heaviest? (the fridge)

■ Tell me the animals in order heaviest to lightest. (whale, elephant, horse, dog, bird, bee)

■ How many animals are heavier than the dog? (3) What are they? (whale, elephant and horse)

↑ Which object is lighter than the microwave oven but heavier than the saucepan? (toaster)

↑ What can you tell me about the weight of the horse compared to the other animals?
(e.g. It is lighter than the whale and elephant, but heavier than the dog, bird and bee.)

Measures

- Understand and use the vocabulary related to mass.
- Compare two masses by direct comparison; extend to more than two.

Date _____

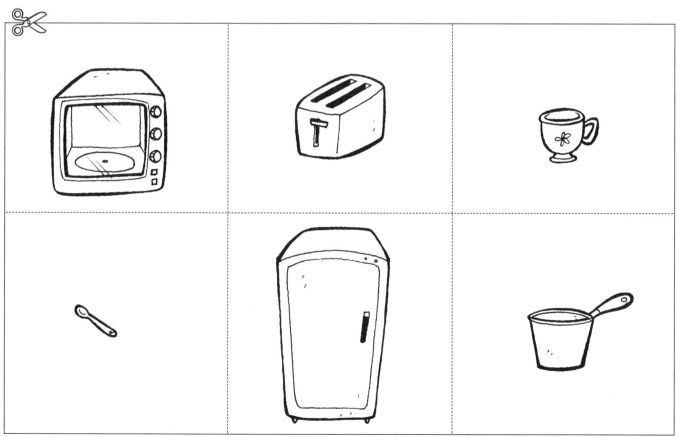

Measures

- Understand and use the vocabulary related to capacity.
- Compare two capacities by direct comparison; extend to more than two.

Resources

Provide each child with the following:

- a copy of Activity 24 pupil sheet
- a red, blue, green and yellow coloured pencil or crayon
- a pair of scissors

Key words

amount   holds   greatest   least   full   empty   half full

Say to the children:

Listen carefully.

I am going to tell you some things to do.

I will say them only once, so listen very carefully.

Do only the things you are told to do and nothing else.

If you make a mistake, cross it out. Do not use an eraser.

There are 9 parts to this activity.

The activity

1. Look at the six objects at the top of the sheet. Which object can hold the greatest amount of water? Colour that object blue.

2. Look at the objects at the top of the sheet again. Which object can hold the least amount of water? Colour that object red.

3. Look at the jugs at the bottom of the sheet. Which jug is full? Colour that jug green.

4. Look at the jugs at the bottom of the sheet again. Which jug is empty? Write your name inside that jug.

5. Again, look at the jugs at the bottom of the sheet. Which jug is half full? Colour that jug yellow.

6. Cut out the objects at the top of the sheet.

7. Arrange the objects in order from the one that can hold the least amount of water to the one that can hold the greatest amount of water.

8. Now cut out the containers at the bottom of the sheet.

9. Arrange the jugs in order from the one that has the greatest amount of water in it to the one that has the least amount of water in it.

Discussion questions

⬇ Look at the objects at the top of the sheet. Which object can hold the greatest amount of water? (swimming pool)

⬇ Look at the jugs at the bottom of the sheet. Which jug is half full? (yellow jug)

■ How many jugs have more water in them than the jug you coloured yellow? (3)

■ Look at the objects at the top of the sheet. Does the watering can hold more or less water than the jug? (more)

⬆ Compare the amount of water the swimming pool, the cup and the wash basin can hold. (e.g. The wash basin can hold more water than the cup, but less water than the swimming pool.)

⬆ Look at the objects at the top of the sheet. Tell me the objects in order from the one that can hold the greatest amount of water to the one that can hold the least amount of water. (swimming pool, bath tub, wash basin, watering can, jug, cup)

Answers

Measures

- Understand and use the vocabulary related to capacity.
- Compare two capacities by direct comparison; extend to more than two.

Date _____

Measures

- Understand and use the vocabulary related to time.
- Order familiar events in time.

Resources

Provide each child with the following:
- a copy of Activity 25 pupil sheet
- a pair of scissors

Key words

before   after   order   last

Say to the children:

Listen carefully.

I am going to tell you some things to do.

I will say them only once, so listen very carefully.

Do only the things you are told to do and nothing else.

There are 4 parts to this activity.

The activity

1. Cut out all the pictures on the sheet.

2. Place the pictures on the table in front of you.

   I am going to tell you a story. As I tell you the story I want you to move the pictures so that they are in the same order as the story.

3. Leo the kitten was a mischievous kitten. Every morning Leo would jump on Harry's bed and wake him up.

   After Harry got ready for school, he would take Leo downstairs and give him his bowl of milk.

   Every morning Leo would spill his milk.

   Every morning Harry would have to wipe it up.

   During the day, while Harry was at school, Leo would run around the house. He was always knocking things over.

   When Harry came home from school, Leo wanted to play. While Harry tried to do his homework, Leo would jump on the table and climb all over Harry's books.

   After Harry had done his homework he liked to watch television. Every afternoon, Leo would climb all over Harry and try to get him to play.

   The only time that Leo was not mischievous was at night. After all his running around all day, Leo would crawl in beside Harry and they would fall asleep together.

4. Write your name on the back of the last picture.

Answers

Discussion questions

↓ Which picture do you have first? (Leo jumping on Harry's bed and waking him up)

↓ What did Leo do while Harry was at school? (He knocked things over.)

■ What did Harry do before he watched television? (He did his homework.)

■ What happened after Harry gave Leo his milk? (Leo spilt it.)
  What did Harry have to do then? (wipe it up)

↑ Tell me the story of Harry and Leo in your own words.

↑ Rearrange the pictures to tell a different version of the story.

Measures

- Understand and use the vocabulary related to time.
- Order familiar events in time.

Date _____

Measures

- Understand and use the vocabulary related to time.
- Know the days of the week and the seasons of the year.

Resources

Provide each child with the following:

- a copy of Activity 26 pupil sheet
- a red, blue, green and yellow coloured pencil or crayon

Key words

today   tomorrow   yesterday   Monday, Tuesday…Sunday
weekend   seasons   spring, summer, autumn, winter   next   after

Say to the children:

Listen carefully.

I am going to tell you some things to do.

I will say them only once, so listen very carefully.

Do only the things you are told to do and nothing else.

If you make a mistake, cross it out. Do not use an eraser.

There are 8 parts to this activity.

The activity

1. Look at the days of the week at the top of the sheet. If today is Thursday, what day will it be tomorrow? Colour that day blue.

2. If today is Wednesday, what day was it yesterday? Colour that day green.

3. Which two days make up the weekend? Colour those days yellow.

4. What day is it today? Draw a ring around that day.

5. Look at the pictures of the four seasons. Draw a ring around the picture that is about spring.

6. Which season comes after spring? Write your name under the picture that shows that season.

7. Now look at the names of the seasons at the bottom of the sheet. Which word says winter? Colour that word red.

8. Which season comes after summer? Draw a cross through the word that says that season.

Answers

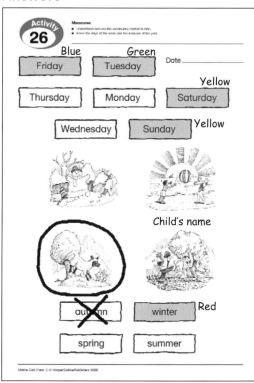

Discussion questions

⬇ What day is it today? What day was it yesterday? What day will it be tomorrow?

⬇ Which season did you draw a ring around? (spring)

■ How many days are there in one week? (7)

■ Which two days make up the weekend? (Saturday and Sunday)
What is the next day called? (Monday)

⬆ Which day is between Tuesday and Thursday? (Wednesday)

⬆ Which season are we in at the moment? Which season will be next?

Measures
- Understand and use the vocabulary related to time.
- Know the days of the week and the seasons of the year.

Date _____

Friday	Tuesday

Thursday	Monday	Saturday

Wednesday	Sunday

autumn	winter

spring	summer

Activity 27

Measures

- Understand and use the vocabulary related to time.
- Read the time to the hour or half hour on analogue clocks.

Resources

Provide each child with the following:
- a copy of Activity 27 pupil sheet
- a red, blue, green and yellow coloured pencil or crayon

Key words

time   clock   o'clock   half past

Say to the children:

Listen carefully.

I am going to tell you some things to do.

I will say them only once, so listen very carefully.

Do only the things you are told to do and nothing else.

If you make a mistake, cross it out. Do not use an eraser.

There are 12 parts to this activity.

The activity

1. Find the clock that says half past three. Colour it blue.

2. Find the clock that says six o'clock. Colour it green.

3. Draw a ring around the clock that says one o'clock.

4. Find the clock that says half past seven. Draw a cross through it.

5. Find Clock c. Make the clock read half past twelve.

6. Find the clock that says half past six. Write your name above it.

7. Find the clock that says four o'clock. Colour it red.

8. Find Clock g. Make it read two o'clock.

9. Find the clock that says half past ten. Colour it yellow.

10. Find the clock that says nine o'clock. Draw a line under it.

11. Find the clock that says eleven o'clock. Ring the letter beside the clock.

12. Find Clock l. Make it read half past five.

Answers

Discussion questions

↓ Tell me any time on the sheet. What letter is it?

↓ How many clocks show an o'clock time? (6)

■ What time does clock e read? (half past 3)

■ Which time is coloured green? (6 o'clock)

↑ Look at Clock h. What time will it read in half an hour's time? (7 o'clock)

↑ Look at Clock f. What time does it read? (9 o'clock)
   Which clock shows what time it will be in two hours' time? (Clock i)

Measures
- Understand and use the vocabulary related to time.
- Read the time to the hour or half hour on analogue clocks.

Date _____

Year 1 Measures, shape and space

Shape and space

■ Use everyday language to describe features of common 2-D shapes.

Resources

Provide each child with the following:
■ a copy of Activity 28 pupil sheet
■ a red, blue, green and yellow coloured pencil or crayon

Key words

square rectangle triangle circle star length round
points corners short long

Say to the children:
Listen carefully.
I am going to tell you some things to do.
I will say them only once, so listen very carefully.
Do only the things you are told to do and nothing else.
If you make a mistake, cross it out. Do not use an eraser.
There are 10 parts to this activity.

The activity

1. Look at the shapes. Find the shape that has four sides of the same length. Colour that shape red.

2. Look at the shape you have just coloured red. Find the name of that shape at the bottom of the sheet and colour it red.

3. Look at the shapes again. Find the shape that is round. Colour that shape blue.

4. Look at the shape you have just coloured blue. Find the name of that shape at the bottom of the sheet and colour it blue.

5. Look at the shapes again. Find the shape that has five points. Colour that shape green.

6. Look at the shape you have just coloured green. Find the name of that shape at the bottom of the sheet and colour it green.

7. Look at the shapes again. Find the shape that has four corners and two short and two long sides. Colour that shape yellow.

8. Look at the shape you have just coloured yellow. Find the name of that shape at the bottom of the sheet and colour it yellow.

9. Look at the shapes again. Find the shape that has three corners and three sides. Write your name inside that shape.

10. Look at the shape you have just written your name inside. Find the name of that shape at the bottom of the sheet and draw a cross through it.

Answers

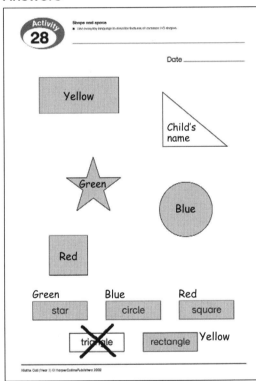

Discussion questions

↓ Which shape did you colour green? (star)

↓ What colour is the circle? (blue)

■ Which two shapes have four sides? (square and rectangle)
How are they different? (All four sides of a square are the same length. The opposite sides of a rectangle are the same length.)

■ Describe a triangle to me.

↑ Tell me something that is shaped like a circle/rectangle.

↑ Does anyone know the name of any other shapes?

Activity 28

Date _____

star	circle	square

triangle	rectangle

Shape and space

■ Use everyday language to describe features of common 3-D shapes.

Resources

Provide each child with the following:
■ a copy of Activity 29 pupil sheet
■ a red, blue, green and yellow coloured pencil or crayon

Key words

cube cuboid sphere cylinder cone pyramid edges
corners base point square rectangular circular faces
curved flat

Say to the children:

Listen carefully.

I am going to tell you some things to do.

I will say them only once, so listen very carefully.

Do only the things you are told to do and nothing else.

If you make a mistake, cross it out. Do not use an eraser.

There are 12 parts to this activity.

The activity

1. Look at the shapes. Find the shape that has no edges or corners. Colour that shape red.

2. Look at the shape you have just coloured red. Find the name of that shape at the bottom of the sheet and colour it red.

3. Look at the shapes again. Find the shape that has a round base and a point at the top. Colour that shape blue.

4. Look at the shape you have just coloured blue. Find the name of that shape at the bottom of the sheet and colour it blue.

5. Look at the shapes again. Find the shape that has six rectangular faces. Colour that shape green.

6. Look at the shape you have just coloured green. Find the name of that shape at the bottom of the sheet and colour it green.

7. Look at the shapes again. Find the shape that has one curved face and two flat circular faces. Colour that shape yellow.

8. Look at the shape you have just coloured yellow. Find the name of that shape at the bottom of the sheet and colour it yellow.

9. Look at the shapes again. Find the shape that has five faces and a point at the top. Draw a line under that shape.

10. Look at the shape you have just drawn a line under. Find the name of that shape at the bottom of the sheet and draw a line under it.

11. Look at the shapes again. Find the shape that has eight corners and six square faces. Write your name inside that shape.

12. Look at the shape you have just written your name inside. Find the name of that shape at the bottom of the sheet and draw a cross through it.

Answers

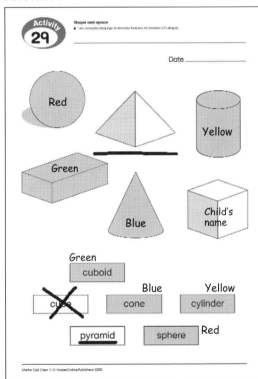

Discussion questions

↓ Which shape did you colour yellow? (cylinder)

↓ What colour is the cone? (blue)

■ Which two shapes have six faces? (cube and a cuboid)
How are they different? (The six faces of a cube are squares. The six faces of a cuboid are rectangles.)

■ Describe a pyramid to me.

↑ Tell me something that is shaped like a sphere/cube.

↑ Do you know the names of any other shapes?

Shape and space

■ Use everyday language to describe features of common 3-D shapes.

Date _____

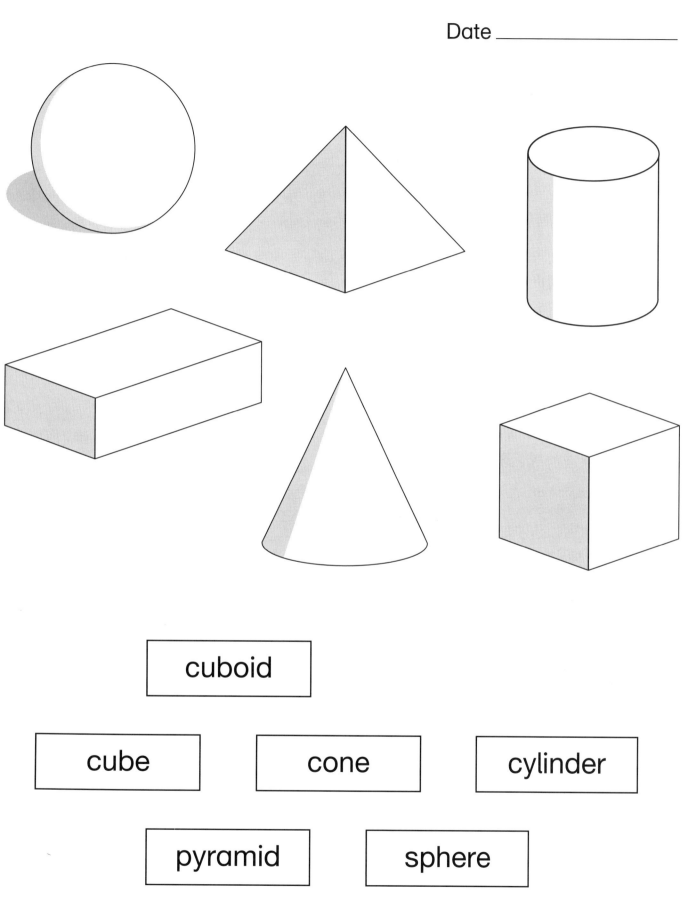

cuboid

cube

cone

cylinder

pyramid

sphere

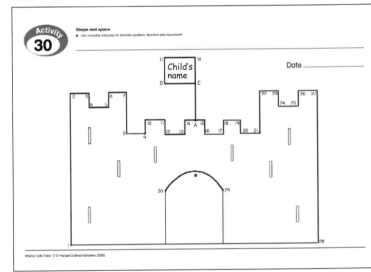

Activity 30

Shape and space

■ Use everyday language to describe position, direction and movement.

Resources

Provide each child with the following:
■ a copy of Activity 30 pupil sheet
■ a pencil

Key words

over   above   under   below   down   left   right   across   star

Say to the children:

Listen carefully.

I am going to tell you some things to do.

I will say them only once, so listen very carefully.

Do only the things you are told to do and nothing else.

If you make a mistake, cross it out. Do not use an eraser.

There are 6 parts to this activity.

The activity

In a moment the instructions will start. You must keep drawing a line as the instructions are given. Do not lift your pencil from the sheet until you are told to do so.

1. Place your pencil on dot 1. Draw a line over 2, over 3, under 4, under 5, over 6, over 7, to the right of 8, to dot 9. Now you can lift your pencil from the sheet.

2. Put your pencil on dot 21. Draw a line over 22 to the right of 23, below 24, below 25, above 26, above 27, down to the left of 28 and across to dot 1. Lift your pencil from the sheet.

3. Put your pencil on dot 9. Draw a line over 10, over 11, under 12, under 13, above 14, above 15, below 16, below 17, over 18, over 19, under 20 to dot 21. Now lift your pencil from the sheet again.

4. Put your pencil on dot 29. Draw a line above the star to dot 30. Lift up your pencil.

5. Put your pencil on dot A. Draw a line past dot E to the left of B, the right of C, the right of D to dot E. Lift up your pencil.

6. Write your name inside the flag.

Answers

Discussion questions

↓ What have you drawn? (castle)

↓ When did you realise that you were drawing a castle?

■ What is a similar word to over? (above)
What word could you use instead of below? (under)

■ Describe for me how you drew the door to the castle.

↑ Give me instructions to draw the castle's flag.

↑ Describe to me how you would get from our classroom to the school office.

Shape and space

■ Use everyday language to describe position, direction and movement.

Date _____

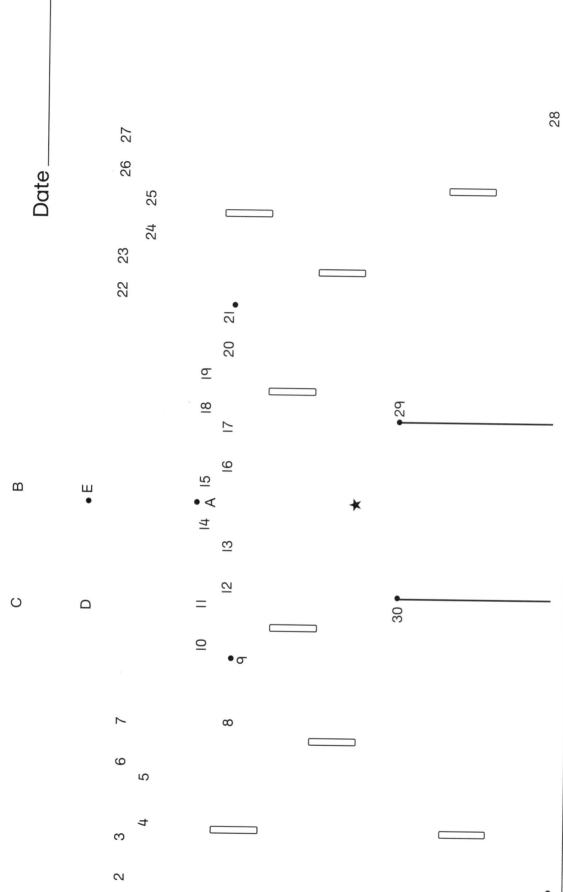